_L_OOKING AT _P_AINTINGS

Circus

Clowness, 1899
Henri de Toulouse-Lautrec, French (1864–1901)

LOOKING AT PAINTINGS

Circus

Peggy Roalf

Series Editor
Jacques Lowe

Designer
Joseph Guglietti

Belitha Press
London

A
JACQUES LOWE
VISUAL ARTS PROJECTS
BOOK

Text © 1993 by Jacques Lowe Visual Arts Projects Inc.
A Jacques Lowe Visual Arts Projects Book

Printed in Italy

First published in the United States By Hyperion Books for Children.

First published in 1993 in the United Kingdom by

🦉 Belitha Press Ltd
31 Newington Green, London N16 9PU.

Cataloguing-in-Print data available from the British Library

ISBN 1 855 61 202 X

Original design concept by Amy Hill
UK Project editor: Jill Laidlaw
UK Editor: Kate Scarborough

Contents

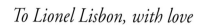

To Lionel Lisbon, with love

Introduction

LOOKING AT PAINTINGS is a series of books about understanding what great artists see when they paint. Painters have been inspired by the skill and spectacle of the circus, with its daring trapeze artists, riotous clowns and dancing bears. Some painters have recreated the excitement that unfolds night after night under the big top. Others have used the circus as a way of expressing other aspects of life, like the tragedy of war.

The fun of the circus can be seen in the paintings by the following artists: Edgar Degas chose a view from below to recreate the experience of craning his neck to watch Miss La La perform under the shining gaslight of the Cirque Fernando (on page 15); Henri de Toulouse-Lautrec (page 23) adopted a strong and bold style to show a ringmaster urging a trick rider to speed up the action; John Steuart Curry, while travelling with America's biggest circus, captured the speed and confidence of the Flying Codonas' death-defying triple somersault (see page 35); a seventeenth-century Indian artist named Bulaqi depicted two elephants displaying their battle skills in *Shah Jahan Watching an Elephant Fight* (on page 9), a jewel-like painting that captures the splendour of a royal entertainment.

The sadness that can be found in figures of fun is brought out by Karl Hofer. He portrayed three solemn clowns in *Masquerade* to express his sadness during the darkest period of World War I (page 29). Max Beckmann painted bold black outlines and harsh colours in *Acrobat on a Trapeze*, a self-portrait that reveals the artist's uncertainty about his fate during the Nazi invasion of Holland in the 1940s (page 38).

Great artists have put their vision of the circus on to canvas creating images of fantasy, images of delight, and sometimes, images of fear.

Note: words in **bold** are explained in the glossary on page 46.

SHAH JAHAN WATCHING AN ELEPHANT FIGHT, about 1639
Bulaqi and unknown artist, Indian (dates unknown), opaque water-colour
and gold on paper, 38 x 23.5 cm

*E*lephants have inspired kings as well as painters. Shah Jahan, a seventeenth-century emperor of India, was thrilled by the spectacle of trumpeting elephants charging in battle. He often arranged elephant fights at his palace to entertain important visitors.

History in paintings

Shah Jahan, best known as the builder of the magnificent Taj Mahal, kept an illustrated history of his reign in an **album** of small paintings called a *padshah-nameh*. A team of artists, each with a particular talent, painted images of wars, festivals and wildlife for the emperor's pleasure. In this picture, Bulaqi, who specialized in painting animals, illustrates an organized elephant fight.

Bulaqi's technique

Bulaqi first drew the scene with black ink and a fine brush. He then covered the entire page with **opaque** white **water-colour** paint thin enough to allow the ink drawing underneath to show through. On top of this Bulaqi painted with rich opaque colours and real gold. The first layer of white paint acts as a kind of reflector, which gives the colours on top an extra brightness.

Look at how all the faces are drawn. They are either in full profile or quarter profile. None of them are facing the front. The buildings are drawn in layers, but there is no feeling of depth in the picture. Bulaqi was not using the techniques of **perspective** that were popular in Europe at the same time. The painting not only shows the elephant fight, but also the levels of importance of each person. The higher the character in the picture the more important he is. In the top windows are the Shah and his most respected guests.

PIERROT, CALLED GILLES, 1718-19
Antoine Watteau, French (1684–1721), oil on canvas, 184 x 149 cm

In 1702, Antoine Watteau left Flanders for Paris, France, with bold ambitions but very little money. At first he worked in an art factory, where dozens of poorly paid artists turned out cheap religious paintings by the dozen. As his skills improved, Watteau found better painting jobs, including scenic design for the theatre. By 1715 he was recognized as a master artist and praised for his beautiful paintings. They were extremely fashionable during this period, because they showed romantic scenes with graceful **architecture** and rich costumes.

Painting different clothes

In *Pierrot*, Watteau used a wide range of colours and textures. He added touches of red, yellow and reddy brown to every colour on his palette, which gave a warm **tone** to this painting. With fine brushes, he painted yellow and mauve shadows to show the folds and buttons of Pierrot's doeskin jacket, which, as a result, looks softer than velvet. Watteau captured light shimmering on the satin trousers with pearly highlights that stand out from pale copper shadows. He brought out the warm tones in the white costume with rose ribbons on the shoes, a scarlet jacket on a background actor and a reddish brown tone in the landscape. The feel of Pierrot's clothes is very different to the leafy trees in the background.

Establishing a reputation

Today most experts believe that Watteau painted this portrait as a theatrical poster for a friend who was a famous actor. In 1805 the rediscovery of this painting—which had disappeared from public view for nearly a hundred years after Watteau died—gave new life to Watteau's reputation as an artist.

Giovanni Battista Tiepolo (1696-1770) drew a series of 104 ink drawings showing a travelling circus led by a character named Pulcinella.

THE STROLLING PLAYERS, about 1793
Francisco de Goya, Spanish (1746–1828), oil on tin plate, 27.5 x 32 cm

Francisco de Goya finally became the official painter to King Charles III of Spain in 1789. But first he worked as an assistant to well-known Spanish artists. Then he taught at the Royal Academy in Madrid. After twenty years his talent finally gained him acceptance in the Spanish court. In 1793, Goya took time off from painting for the king. During this time, he painted a series of pictures about Spain's best-loved entertainments for his personal enjoyment.

On the dwarf's costume, Goya painted delicate white lines as highlights. His glass is only a few dots of white!

Travelling theatre

In *The Strolling Players*, Goya shows a group of actors standing on a makeshift stage. Because they are a travelling group, they will have taken their props and stage with them to set up wherever they would find a good audience. A raised stage is divided by a curtained screen behind which the actors would go when not needed on stage. Look carefully and you can see another of the actors peeping out from behind the curtains.

Broad and delicate brushstrokes

Goya painted the background in broad strokes of grey-green that emphasize the rich colours in the costumes worn by the actors. In contrast, Goya gave Harlequin a bright, multicoloured clownsuit painted with delicate brushstrokes. The dwarf is dressed in a swirl of satin stripes. Columbine's lovely face (she is the only woman on stage) is framed by a lace collar with gleaming highlights so thickly painted that they stand up from the canvas.

13

MISS LA LA AT THE CIRQUE FERNANDO, 1879
Edgar Degas, French (1834–1917), oil on canvas, 116.7 x 77.4 cm

The dazzling Cirque Fernando attracted the whole of Paris when it opened in 1877. For Edgar Degas, the rope dancers and trick riders provided the most wonderful movement and colour. To Degas, it was as thrilling as the ballet and horse racing, which were his favourite subjects. Degas was particularly fascinated by the daring Miss La La, who twirled in the air suspended by her teeth from a rope above the audience.

Finding the best angle

First Degas made a series of drawings from every angle to study the acrobat's spinning figure. Using his drawings, Degas then constructed the form of both the acrobat and the soaring space of the circus dome in this painting. Form is a word often confused with shape. It means all of the qualities that describe a person or object, including size, weight, colour, shape, texture, tone and movement.

Using few colours

Degas avoided adding distracting details like the audience to concentrate on the action. He also reduced his **palette** to a few contrasting colours, pink, green, yellow and lavender. He enlivened Miss La La's costume with lavender shadows to suggest a satin texture. He painted the walls in patches of salmon pink and tan that echo the peach flesh tone of her tights. Degas painted the ribbing of the vaulted ceiling in a light green that goes well with the pink walls. The bright lighting scheme recreates the theatre's dazzling gaslight. With a white highlight on the rope, he is able to show the great distance between Miss La La and the ground.

*James Tissot (1836-1902), a friend and contemporary of Degas, was inspired by a team of beautiful charioteers at the Cirque Fernando. Through the process of **etching**, he was able to create precisely-drawn figures, which he filled out with velvety dark shadows.*

JUGGLERS AT THE CIRQUE FERNANDO, 1879
Pierre-Auguste Renoir (1841–1919), oil on canvas, 131.3 x 101 cm

In 1879, Pierre-Auguste Renoir found himself deeply in debt. For two years he had struggled to pay rent on a second painting studio with a garden. He needed a garden so that he could paint in natural light. To keep his garden, Renoir had to attract rich Parisians for portrait **commissions.**

With fine overlapping ink lines called **cross-hatching, Pablo Picasso** (1881-1973) drew the powerful back of a strong man effortlessly lifting a tiny acrobat into the air.

An advertisement
To show people that he could paint portraits, Renoir went to the circus. In *Jugglers at the Cirque Fernando,* Renoir adapted his painting style to make it more realistic. Renoir captured the fun of the circus by using lots of different shades of yellow. The ground is painted with contrasting colours of coral, green and lavender paint that turn into a cool yellow. Lemon yellow—the brightest shade—makes the performers' shoes and hair ribbons stand out against the background. With small, nearly invisible brushstrokes, Renoir depicted the lovely faces of the young jugglers.

A new perspective
Instead of using traditional methods of perspective to create a setting that looks realistic, Renoir painted this picture from above, and so made a smaller background for the two girls. He gave the scene depth by placing five oranges in a diagonal path on the ground to lead the viewer's eyes toward the distance.

Renoir's advertisement was successful. When this painting was exhibited in 1879, it attracted wealthy Parisians who paid Renoir well. He was able to keep his garden.

CARNIVAL EVENING, 1886
Henri Rousseau, French (1844–1910), oil on canvas, 116.7 x 89 cm

Henri Rousseau, who worked as a poorly-paid customs clerk, was called *Le Douanier*, a French term that means 'customhouse official', by his artist friends. These artists and poets gave him this title out of respect and because they found it funny that he could only paint on his one day off after working a seventy-hour week.

Creating depth

In this imaginary scene a full moon casts silvery light on two clowns strolling under an immense sky. Although the figures seem almost as flat as paper cut-outs, Rousseau created a feeling of depth by using light and dark colours. He painted the figures in **pastel** colours that stand out against the nearly black ground. The trees get lighter in colour the further back they are in the landscape. Delicate tints of rose, blue and gold in the distance draw the viewer's eyes from the figures into the trees, darkly silhouetted against the light.

An air of mystery

Rousseau creates an air of mystery through the connections and contrasts between the tiny figures and the vast sky. The pink tone glowing through the blue sky is repeated in highlights on the costumes. By emphasizing the great scale of the heavens, Rousseau makes the clown and his girlfriend seem small and insignificant. The viewer is left wondering what they are doing in such a deserted place at this time of night. Is their love a secret?

Winning approval

A Carnival Evening was the first painting that *Le Douanier* Rousseau publicly exhibited. His special style, expressed in magical paintings such as this one, won the admiration of fellow artists like the famous Pablo Picasso (see page 16) and **Paul Gauguin**. However, this approval was not widespread. Others thought that Rousseau would have done better to remain a customs clerk.

BAREBACK RIDERS, 1886
W. H. Brown, American (dates unknown), oil on cardboard, 47 x 62 cm

The first American circus performance took place in 1785 when a horseman from the American state of Philadelphia named Thomas Pool presented a trick-riding exhibition that captivated the public's imagination. In 1880 several small circuses in New York State joined together to form the travelling three-ring extravaganza called Barnum and Bailey's Greatest Show on Earth. W. H. Brown, a painter who lived at that time in Binghamton, New York, was inspired by a team that took acrobatic riding to daring new heights.

The unknown artist

We know little about Brown—not even whether the artist was a man or a woman. Only four paintings signed by the artist have survived, two of which are circus scenes. However, we are fairly sure that the artist had no art school training. This style of painting can be called **folk art**, because there is little traditional perspective in the picture.

Focusing on the performance

Brown draws attention to the amazing performance by making the trick riders unusually large compared with the horse and the clown. The performers' costumes are painted with sharp details compared to the faceless audience. With fine brushstrokes the artist depicted gold embroidery on the man's red suit; blue satin and lace on the woman's tutu; stars, stripes, and zigzag ruffles on the clown's pyjamas.

IN THE CIRQUE FERNANDO: THE RINGMASTER, 1888
Henri de Toulouse-Lautrec (1864–1901), oil on canvas, 100 x 161 cm

As a teenager, Henri de Toulouse-Lautrec had a couple of riding accidents which left him permanently handicapped. Because he came from an aristocratic family, he should have been a soldier. But as a result of his disability, he immersed himself in the study of painting. The exciting world of Parisian entertainments, especially the dance halls and the circus, became the focus of Toulouse-Lautrec's life and the subject of his work.

A bold picture

Toulouse-Lautrec drew a bold **composition** based on the circles in the grandstand and the ring of the Cirque Fernando. He created the effect of depth by exaggerating the size of the performers in the foreground compared with the spectators in the distance. The picture is abruptly cut off at the edges (or cropped) to spotlight a cantering horse and its rider.

Solid forms

Toulouse-Lautrec painted expressive shapes, lines and flat areas of colour rather than shading and highlights to create the appearance of solid forms. With sharply observed lines, he depicted the rider's slim but powerful arms and legs. He emphasized the bold style of this painting with contrasting black and white and a palette of muted green, mauve and dark red.

In this painting, Toulouse-Lautrec captured the circus atmosphere in a style that, in the twentieth century, would make him one of the most admired and copied artists.

Georges Rouault (1871-1958) suggested the speed of a juggler's routine with a blurred arc of reddish-brown colour at the top of the picture.

THE CIRCUS, 1891

Georges Seurat, French (1859–91), oil on canvas, 182.7 x 147.8 cm

Georges Seurat was fascinated by the new ways of using colour. Through his studies he developed a method of painting that was later called pointillism: painting with dots of colour. The tiny spots of pure, unmixed colour blend in the viewer's eye when seen from a metre away. In 1886, Seurat, who had previously painted outdoor scenes with his dots, began to explore ways of obtaining the effects of artificial light in his paintings of Parisian nightlife.

Georges Seurat used line to express different moods. For happiness and activity he painted up-turned curves and for calmness he drew horizontal lines.

Painting movement

In *The Circus*, Seurat drew movement with curving, upturned shapes and bright colours. All of the figures in the foreground are made out of lines sweeping upward, from the trick rider's graceful arms to the acrobat's pointed toes and crescent-shaped grin. The ringmaster's snapping whip is echoed by the clown's yellow banner that swirls out of the picture and back in again to create a feeling of activity. Seurat was able to create many different shades of yellow by adding tiny dots of orange, white and blue paint in varying amounts.

Colours and lines

The detail (left) shows that he produced a rich golden colour by adding specks of orange to the acrobat's costume. Seurat contrasted the curved lines and shapes of the circus performers with a background composed of horizontal bands and right angles. The motionless spectators contrast with the balletic trick rider in the ring.

Seurat died two days after this painting was first exhibited in 1891. He remained unknown to the general public for many years, but, in studios around the world, other painters who admired Seurat's new style collected reproductions of *The Circus.*

25

SOIR BLEU, detail, 1914
Edward Hopper, American (1882–1967), oil on canvas, 91.4 x 182.7 cm

Edward Hopper studied in Paris from 1909 to 1911. In his spare time he enjoyed the outdoor cafés and street life of the romantic French capital. After returning to New York, Hopper painted *Soir Bleu* from his memories of a street carnival called Mi Carême. In a scene painted on to a background the colour of evening blue (the title of the painting means evening blue), Hopper was expressing the despair he felt for the French people who in 1914 were facing the dreadful prospect of World War I.

Hopper's trademark

In the small illustration that shows the entire painting (below), we can see a clown and an entertainer mingle with others on an outdoor terrace. Each character seems absorbed in private thoughts that isolate them from each other. You can tell because none of them look at each other. This is a familiar feature in all of Hopper's art.

The clown

Hopper gave the clown, who dominates the scene, weight and substance with broad areas of white paint marked by simple details. Hopper shaped the clown's strong features with strokes of paint tinted with yellow and grey. Blue-grey shading separates the clown's ruffled collar and jacket. A dark shadow just under his nose suggests the strong light beaming down from above, like a spotlight.

Pretty lanterns that contrast with dark colours emphasize the feeling of sadness that Edward Hopper created in Soir Bleu, *shown here in its entirety.*

The fact that Hopper chose a clown to be the focus of this picture is particularly important. Usually a clown is funny and happy. This one is obviously lonely and sad. He is used to point out that a joyful city has been plunged into gloom because of war.

MASQUERADE, 1922
Karl Hofer, German (1878–1956), oil on canvas, 129 x 102.8 cm

L ike other twentieth-century painters such as Max Beckmann (1884-1950), whose work you can see on page 38, Karl Hofer expressed a bleak view of life. During a badly-timed visit to Paris at the outbreak of World War I, the German painter was imprisoned and treated as an enemy of France. Hofer expressed his despair by painting these three jesters, whose comic acts can be both funny and sad.

Painting the figures

Hofer posed the three figures with the white-suited Pierrot in the middle to emphasize the contrast between dark and bright colours. He painted the clowns standing out against a blue-black background with a patch of yellow behind Harlequin, who wears a suit of multicoloured diamonds. With strokes of orange over wet black paint, Hofer blended the colours directly on the canvas to create the look of velvet in Punch's costume. The artist added broad highlights of pale blue, yellow and mauve on Pierrot's jacket to suggest reflections on shining white satin. With the pointed end of a brush, Hofer scratched crisp outlines around the figures while the thick paint was still wet.

The clowns' expressions

Look at the faces of the clowns and the way that they are huddled together. Can you tell what they are thinking and feeling? The words that spring to mind are fear, suspicion and sadness. However, they all have glorious shapes and colours in their costumes. What do you think the painter is trying to say?

With pencil, George Grosz (1893-1959) created a delicate balance between sharp lines and soft shading in this drawing of a rope dancer.

CLOWN ON A HORSE, 1927
Marc Chagall, Russian (1887–1985), gouache on paper, 66 x 50.7 cm

After a four year stay in Paris from 1910-14, Marc Chagall returned to Russia and was appointed director of a new school of fine arts in his native city, Vitebsk. However, the new government criticized Chagall's imaginative teaching methods and forced his resignation. In 1923, Chagall returned to Paris, the city where he had found success and happiness nine years earlier. He created this painting as a study for a series of etchings on circus themes commissioned by Ambrose Vollard, the well-known publisher of artists' **prints.**

A dream world

Like many of the figures in Chagall's paintings, this happy clown seems to be floating above the horse on a balloon. Chagall uses fanciful patterns and brilliant colours that make the picture very bright. The pretty flowers that seem to grow in the horse's mane also enliven the picture. Red paint on the clown's plume, umbrella and shoes match the multicolour markings on the pony. Chagall creates a dream world with the help of pink and blue cloud forms in the background.

Water-colour

Chagall painted with a type of water-colour paint called **gouache,** which can be used in its opaque form or thinned with water to create **transparent** colours. The clown's yellow jacket and the deep blue background are opaque. They completely cover the paper on which the artist painted. However, Chagall **diluted** white paint to make transparent highlights on the ball. The blue background shows through the ball, emphasizing its spherical form. With opaque yellow and white, and transparent green and blue, Chagall created the cheerful design on the clown's tights.

Chagall affectionately called this series of gouache paintings 'Vollard's circus' in honour of his friend whose continued **patronage** freed the artist from worrying about money.

PIP AND FLIP, 1932
Reginald Marsh, American (1898–1954), tempera on paper mounted on canvas, 122.5 x122.5 cm

Before becoming a painter, Reginald Marsh was an illustrator for magazines and newspapers. He developed great skill in drawing by observing and sketching people on the streets of New York City in the United States. Coney Island, with its circus sideshow, was one of Marsh's favourite subjects. He preferred 'the masses to the classes'. He always chose to paint ordinary people who enjoyed cheap entertainment rather than the well-off people from his own background.

The composition

In *Pip and Flip*, Marsh compared the bustling crowd with the gaudy sideshow advertisements. The motionless, larger-than-life figures on the flat backdrop contrast strongly with the surging throng underneath. The artist anchored this busy composition through a triangular arrangement that comes to a point above the two dancers watching the spectators.

Rather than first drawing the composition in pencil, Marsh painted directly onto the canvas, looking back at drawings he had made of Coney Island. He began by making the figures appear realistic using deep grey paint to create shading. Then Marsh built up colours in thin transparent layers allowing the details of the grey painting underneath to show through in the finished work. Marsh chose to work in **tempera** because the fast-drying paint forced him to work quickly and enabled him to keep the lively spirit of his original sketchbook drawings.

Through this pose, Walt Kuhn (1877-1949) drew this resting clown's weight and fatigue.

In this picture, Marsh has made the spectators the spectacle, and the circus a backdrop to the action.

32

THE FLYING CODONAS, 1932
John Steuart Curry, American (1897–1946), tempera and oil on composition board, 91.4 x 76 cm

Early in his career John Steuart Curry painted scenes of rural American life. However, searching for new inspiration in his work, Curry travelled with the Ringling Brothers Barnum and Bailey Circus for three months in 1932 and found what he was looking for.

Catching the act

In this painting Curry captured the excitement of acrobat Alfredo Codona rocketing through space in a daring triple somersault. Curry illustrated the dizzying height by choosing a view close to the ceiling of the big top. To capture the speed of the action, he painted the Codonas in sharp detail compared to the blurred background. This is an effect often seen in sports photographs when the camera moves to follow the athletes. Curry placed the two figures near the edges of the painting to emphasize the distance between acrobat and catcher as well as the danger of their feat. Both the men are lit up by spotlights. These are painted with transparent **glazes** of white paint and bright yellow on the catcher's orange costume.

Working on tour

During his tour with the circus, Curry filled several sketchbooks with drawings of acrobats, clowns and animal trainers. Later, in his studio, he used these drawings to develop several paintings, including this one, that show the highly trained athletes whose daredevil feats appear effortless.

John Steuart Curry encircled Clyde Beatty, the great lion tamer, with his ferocious cats to dramatize their size, power and numbers.

34

CHARIOT RACE, 1933
Milton Avery, American (1885–1965), oil on canvas, 122 x 182.7 cm

Milton Avery was an American artist who was very influenced by European painters of the time, particularly **Henri Matisse** (1869-1954). Avery is best known for dream-like landscape paintings that seem somewhere between reality and imagination. Like Matisse, Avery used colours rather than elaborate details to express this quality in his work.

The ghostly race

In *Chariot Race*, Avery presents a haunted circus. Two ghostly trapeze artists swing into a scene in which faceless charioteers drive their horses with invisible reins and traces. Clowns and circus animals float strangely through the wierd spectacle.

Preparing for the work

Avery first conjured up this phantom circus as a small water-colour. This worked as a quick sketch to put down his ideas. He then copied it on to this huge canvas in **oil paint**. In this way he recreated the freshness of his vision by referring to his original composition.

To reproduce the same effect as water-colours, Avery used oil paint diluted with **turpentine**. He painted the grey horse with a thin layer of purple. Over this he brushed on a slightly thicker grey, letting the purple tone show through to form shadows on the horse's legs, chest and neck. With crisp lines he shaped its rear leg and tail. Avery used the same technique to paint the white horse and the trick rider, who is tinted with shadows created by the indigo background.

In the background, the curved horizon line defined with wispy cloud-like forms suggests that Avery's circus exists beyond the earth. It is supernatural.

This detail shows a performing seal floating through the blue haze of Milton Avery's imaginary circus scene.

ACROBAT ON TRAPEZE, 1940
Max Beckmann, German (1884–1950), oil on canvas, 146 x 90 cm

After the outbreak of World War II in 1939, Max Beckmann wrote in his diary: "I begin this new notebook in a condition of complete uncertainty about my own existence and the state of our planet. Wherever one looks: chaos and disorder". Beckmann had fled to Amsterdam, Holland, to escape the Nazis in Germany. As Beckmann was preparing to leave for the United States, Hitler's army invaded Holland and the artist was trapped there until 1947. Beckmann painted this self-portrait turning himself into a trapeze artist. This was because he saw his situation as risky, just as a trapeze artist's.

What it means

The daring acrobat perches high above the ground without a net. Painted life-size, the squatting figure nearly fills the canvas. It creates a dramatic contrast to the tiny people far below and suggests the isolation Beckmann felt while he was cut off from his own country.

Beckmann creates a mood of anxiety by painting jagged forms. He boldly outlined the acrobat with black paint, breaking the figure into angular green, purple and yellow shapes. Using a technique called **impasto**, Beckmann created rough textures in the thick surface of the paint with a palette knife and stiff brushes. He emphasized the tense atmosphere through the sharp contrast of black shadows on the figure and a yellow background.

Ben Shahn (1898-1969) used a pen to draw lines that connect the figures of this packed circus.

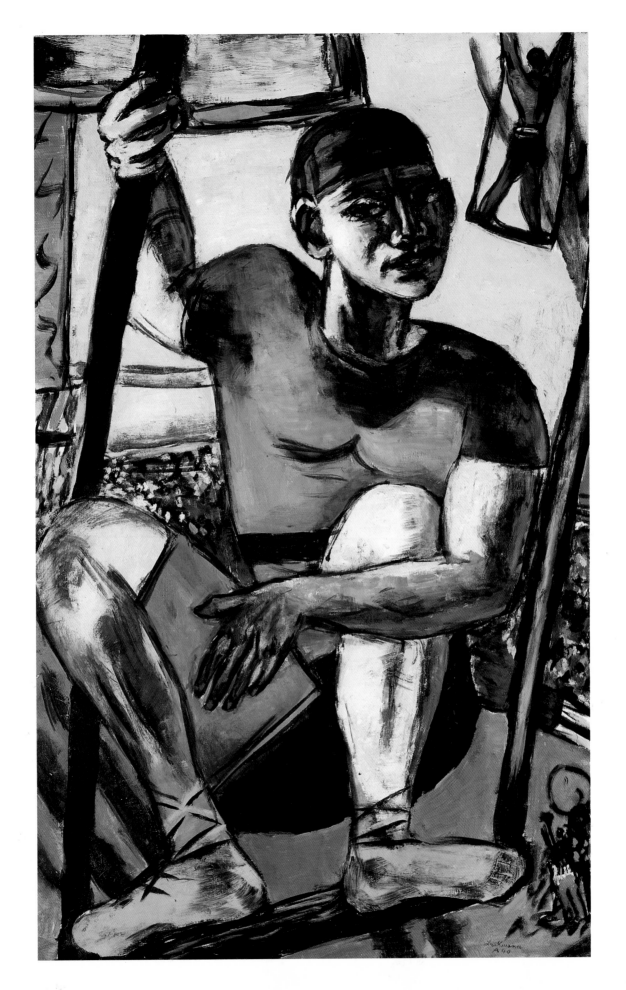

CIRCUS ELEPHANTS, 1941
John Marin, American (1870–1953), crayon and wash on paper, 48 x 62 cm

The elephant is one of the most popular acts in all circuses. Whether leading the circus parade, lifting beautiful dancers into the air with their trunks, or raising the poles of the big top, circus elephants have inspired American painters for almost two hundred years.

John Marin, famous for seascape paintings that express the changing moods of weather with powerful shapes, turned to a more realistic style in 1932. He began a series of circus scenes and created this joyous celebration of the elephant.

Real and abstract

In this painting seven elephants parade in the centre ring. Marin focuses our attention on the animals by painting both **abstract** and realistic details. The abstract is the human audience in the background painted with simple patches of primary colours, whereas the performing elephants are painted realistically. At the bottom of the picture, Marin scribbled in an audience of almost abstract elephants with dashing strokes of paint.

Robert Riggs (dates unknown) chose a worm's-eye view to emphasize the huge size of this herd of dancing elephants.

Washes

Marin used water-colour in different degrees of wetness. He drew the flowing curves of the animals with brown paint and a fine wet brush. When the lines had dried, he emphasized their jumbo forms with **washes** of brown and blue tones.

The pale yellow ground is also painted in wash, whereas a red stroke denoting the ring and blue strokes in the foreground are in soft **crayon.** Marin suggests the excitement and constant activity of the circus with curved lines, spots and spatters of colour.

THREE CLOWNS IN A RING, 1944
George Schreiber (born 1904), water-colour on paper, 57 x 67.9 cm

Madcap clowns have enchanted George Schreiber since his childhood in Belgium. After completing his training in Europe, Schreiber moved to New York City. When his daughter Joan was born in 1947, Schreiber wrote and illustrated a book for her called *Bambino the Clown*. Bambino makes a special appearance as the ringmaster in this painting, which the artist based on his memories of European clowns that romped through the audience to amuse the children.

Schreiber chose a trapeze artist's view of the ring for *Three Clowns in a Ring* to depict a frenzied scene. The clown on the left catapults through the air towards the ring where eight horses race at a wild gallop. Another clown seems to be upsetting a stunt bareback rider!

Keeping the paper wet
Schreiber painted this picture with a water-colour technique that depends upon working rapidly while the paper is wet. He created soft shadows on Bambino's trousers by applying dark reddy brown over wet brown paint.

Pastel colours and musical notes enliven Jean Dufy's (1877-1953) painting of a circus band.

He left areas of paper blank for the white horses and added shading and details with grey. Schreiber created the effect of colourful stage lighting through a wash of brilliant red in the background. After the paper had dried, he added the pattern on the airborne clown's shirt and the horses' feathers and bridles.

In this tribute to clowns, Schreiber turns the circus over to the funny and clumsy characters from his childhood who lived on in his imagination.

CLOWN WITH A PIGEON, 1989
Krishna Reddy, Indian (born 1925), colour engraving, 40 x 30 cm

Krishna Reddy sees circus clowns as artists and magicians. His love of clowns began in the small open-air theatres he enjoyed as a child in India. The performers were often friends and neighbours from his own village, taking part in the festivities and sharing the fun.

In this print, Reddy shows a magician clown conjuring up a pigeon from the air. To produce this picture, Reddy carved the image with sharp tools onto a flat slab of metal making it a printing plate. He scratched lines around the figures and textured patterns on the clown's jacket. Reddy also transferred photographic images onto the metal, such as the clown's hands and the bird. He then applied coloured inks—red, blue, yellow and black—to the plate. Using a **printing press**, Reddy created ten identical impressions onto sheets of paper.

Before Reddy had developed this new method of printing all of his colours at once, most artists found printmaking very hard work. It required a different plate for each colour. Artists could not even see the results of their creativity until every colour had been printed, one plate at a time. With Reddy's technique, all of the colours are transferred from a single plate on to paper in one pass through the press. This enables him to experiment with different colour effects because he can see the finished work immediately.

Yasuo Kuniyoshi (dates unknown) created the rich black tones of this acrobat's costume by drawing with a greasy crayon on to a stone, from which he made a print called a lithograph.

Reddy travels all over the world sharing his knowledge with other artists who make prints. For many painters, printmaking is a way to create lots of pictures of a single image that can be enjoyed by many people.

Glossary and Index

ABSTRACT: form and colour that has no recognizable subject matter.

ALBUM: a blank book into which all sorts of pictures can be placed.

ARCHITECTURE,: (1) a building that has been carefully designed and constructed. (2) the art of designing buildings.

COMMISSION: 1) a work of art produced at the request of a **patron.** 2) the appointment of an artist to create a work of art.

COMPOSITION: the arrangement of objects and figures in a painting and the combination of colours and shapes.

CRAYON: a coloured pencil that can be made from chalk or wax.

CROSS-HATCHING: a drawing technique for shading, using fine criss-crossed lines.

DILUTED: the thinning of a liquid by adding another liquid like water or **turpentine.**

ETCHING: the art of drawing a design on to metal or wood by eating out the lines with acid.

FOLK ART: a term to describe objects or paintings that are made in a traditional way by craftsmen or painters who have had no art school training.

GLAZES: a layer of partly **transparent** colour that gives a glassy finish to the painting.

GOUACHE: this is an **opaque** form of **water-colour** paint, which is also called **tempera** or body colour.

HENRI MATISSE (1869-1954): a French painter, sculptor and designer. He was one of the most influential artists of his time. He believed in using colour to express his feelings and defined form in art.

IMPASTO: a method of painting using very thick layers of paint which keep the marks of the brush. You can apply this paint with anything you like, for example, a knife or your fingers.

OIL PAINT: pigment, the material used to give a colour to paint, is combined with oil (usually linseed or poppy oil). Oil paint is never mixed with water. It is washed off brushes or thinned with **turpentine.** Oils dry slowly, enabling the artist to work on a painting for a long time. Oil paint has been used since the fifteenth century.

OPAQUE: not letting light pass through. Opaque paints conceal what is under them. (The opposite of **transparent**)

PABLO PICASSO (1881-1973): The most famous artist of this century and one of the most influential. He was born in Spain, but moved to Paris in 1904. He was not only a painter, but also a sculptor, a potter and a designer.

PALETTE: (1) a flat tray used by a painter for laying out and mixing colours. (2) the range of colours selected by a painter for a work.

PASTEL: a drawing or painting stick which produces an **opaque** colour. It does not change when applied to paper, as opposed to **water-colour** which will change its colour when dry.

PATRONAGE: a term to describe the usually financial support given by an individual, the patron, to the arts or an artist.

PAUL GAUGUIN (1848-1903): a French painter, sculptor and printmaker. He is known for his bold use of colour.

PERSPECTIVE: perspective is a method of representing people, places and things in a painting or drawing to make them appear solid or realistic rather than flat.

A special technique of perspective, called foreshortening, is used to make figures and objects painted on a flat surface look real. For example, an artist will paint the hand of an outstretched arm larger than it is in proportion to the arm, which becomes smaller as it goes back towards the shoulder. This correction, necessary in a picture using perspective, is automatically made by the human eye looking at a scene in real life. Foreshortening refers to the representation of figures or objects, whereas perspective refers to the representation of a scene or a space.

PRINT: one of many images created by mechanical means from the same original. Prints can be made from a metal plate, from a woodblock, from silk gauze (silkscreen print), or from a stone (lithograph). **Etchings** are traditionally made using a flat sheet of copper called a plate. The artist then inks the plate with a roller and, using a **printing press**, prints the same image onto many sheets of paper.

PRINTING PRESS: a machine with which pictures are made in ink on to paper from etched plates.

TEMPERA: pigment is combined with raw egg yolk to turn it into a thick paste that can be applied with a brush. Tempera was used by the ancient Greeks and was the favourite technique of painters during the medieval period in Europe.

TONE: the colours used overall in a painting. For example, an artist might begin by painting the entire picture in shades of greenish grey. After more colours are applied using transparent glazes, shadows and highlights, the mass of greenish grey colour underneath will show through as an even tone.

TRANSPARENT: allowing light to pass through so colours underneath can be seen. (The opposite of **opaque**)

TURPENTINE: a strong-smelling liquid made from pine sap, used in oil painting. *See also* OIL PAINT.

WASHES: paint that has been mixed with a lot of water to make it very **transparent.**

WATER-COLOUR: pigment is combined with a water-based substance. Water-colour paint is thinned with water, and areas of paper are often left uncovered to produce highlights. Water-colour paint was first used 37,000 years ago by cave dwellers who painted the first wall paintings.

Credits